THIS BLOOMSBURY ACTIVITY BOOK BELONGS TO:

To make history you need to be brave, be bold and believe in yourself just like the women in this book. Adventure through the past with these fantastically great women and see how you can make history!

BLOOMSBURY
CHILDREN'S BOOKS
LONDON OXFORD NEW YORK NEW DELHI SYDNEY

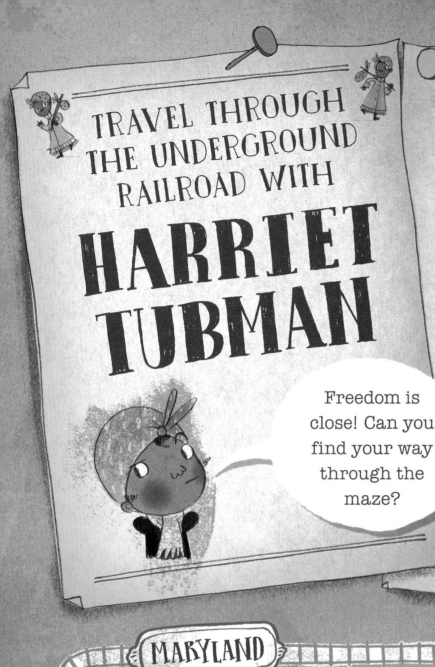

TRAVEL THROUGH THE UNDERGROUND RAILROAD WITH HARRIET TUBMAN

Freedom is close! Can you find your way through the maze?

Harriet Tubman lived during the **1800s** and, like many other African Americans in the south of the USA, she and her family were slaves. Harriet dreamed of a better life and found her way to freedom in 1849 through the Underground Railroad. She then used her freedom to help other slaves escape. Harriet helped so many people to freedom that a reward was offered for her capture!

MARYLAND

START

WANTED

WANTED!

THE UNDERGROUND RAILROAD WAS

NETWORK OF SAFE ROUTES TO FREE STATES.

Lead the crowd with BOUDICCA

Boudicca was queen of the Celtic Iceni tribe. In **43 AD**, the mighty Roman army made a BIG mistake when, just because she was a woman, they underestimated her. The Romans tried to tell Boudicca that they were in charge. But she wasn't afraid of them. She defended her people and inspired her army to fight bravely against injustice.

We're in charge now!

Join the dots to see Boudicca roaring and leading the crowds! Decorate the page with stickers.

STAND UP FOR YOUR RIGHTS WITH
Flora Drummond

In **1906**, Flora Drummond joined the women of the WSPU (Women's Social and Political Union) to fight for the law to be changed so that women could vote too (at the time only men could vote). Flora led marches and even went to the Prime Minister's home to campaign for women's rights. Thanks to Flora and the suffragettes, in 1918 some women over the age of 30 gained the right to vote!

WE WILL GET THE VOTE

YES WE WILL!

go flora

go girls

DEEDS NOT WORDS

TO VICTORY

VOTES for WOMEN

Together We Are Strong

THE WOMEN OF THE WSPU WERE ALSO CALLED 'SUFFRAGETTES'.

Design banners and sashes of your own to stand up for something that you believe in.

CRACK THE CODE WITH

NOOR INAYAT KHAN

Noor Inayat Khan was the first female wireless operator to go to France during **World War Two**. Noor worked as an undercover agent and sent messages to a network of spies working for Britain. She sent over 20 messages which helped evacuate airmen who had been stranded in France. Her efforts were acknowledged with the George Cross medal of honour for bravery.

SECRET CODES

TWENTY JATAKA TALES
BY NOOR INAYAT KHAN

Can you crack the secret codes below? Use the Morse code alphabet to discover Noor's message!

A ·—
B —···
C —·—·
D —··
E ·
F ··—·
G ——·
H ····
I ··
J ·———
K —·—
L ·—··
M ——
N —·

O ———
P ·——·
Q ——·—
R ·—·
S ···
T —
U ··—
V ···—
W ·——
X —··—
Y —·——
Z ——··

1 ·————
2 ··———
3 ···——
4 ····—
5 ·····
6 —····
7 ——···
8 ———··
9 ————·
0 —————

Colour in the
Bookshelf of
BRILLIANCE
Reach for the STARS!
CCCP
Show everyone you can do it.
ADA LOVELACE
VALENTINA TERESHKOVA
POCAHONTAS
NOOR INAYAT KHAN
HATSHEPSUT
Use your IMAGINATION to shape the FUTURE!
You are capable of things you never thought POSSIBLE.
Everybody deserves RESPECT and KINDNESS.

STUDY MEDICINE WITH
DR ELIZABETH BLACKWELL

In **1849**, Elizabeth Blackwell became the first woman to be awarded a medical degree. Elizabeth showed everyone that just because there were no women doctors didn't mean there shouldn't be. Once she had her degree she travelled to France to gain experience and, in 1857, she opened her very own hospital in New York — the New York Infirmary for Women and Children.

TRUST ME! I SHALL become a doctor!

Can you find the matching body parts? Draw a line in between the pairs. One has already been done for you.

BRAVE DETERMINED PIONEER CLEVER BOLD

Dr ELIZABETH BLACKWELL

Reach for the stars with VALENTINA TERESHKOVA

CCCP

VOSTOK 6

In **1962**, Valentina Tereshkova was selected by the Soviet space programme to train as a cosmonaut. Then in 1963, Valentina became the first woman to be launched into space! She spent almost three days there and made 48 orbits of the Earth!

_____

_____

_____

_____

_____

_____

_____

On her amazing journey in outer space, Valentina forgot to take her toothbrush! What would you take up into space with you? Use the space above to make a list of what you would pack. Use stickers to decorate the page!

POCAHONTAS

In **1606**, colonists from Britain arrived to Pocahontas's home. There was a lot of conflict and misunderstanding between Pocahontas's people and the new colonists. Pocahontas tried to make peace and offered them her help and friendship. She believed that all people, no matter what their culture, deserved respect and kindness.

Copy and colour the picture of Pocahontas and the Chief Powhatan. Use the grid as a guide.

Add stickers to the frame.

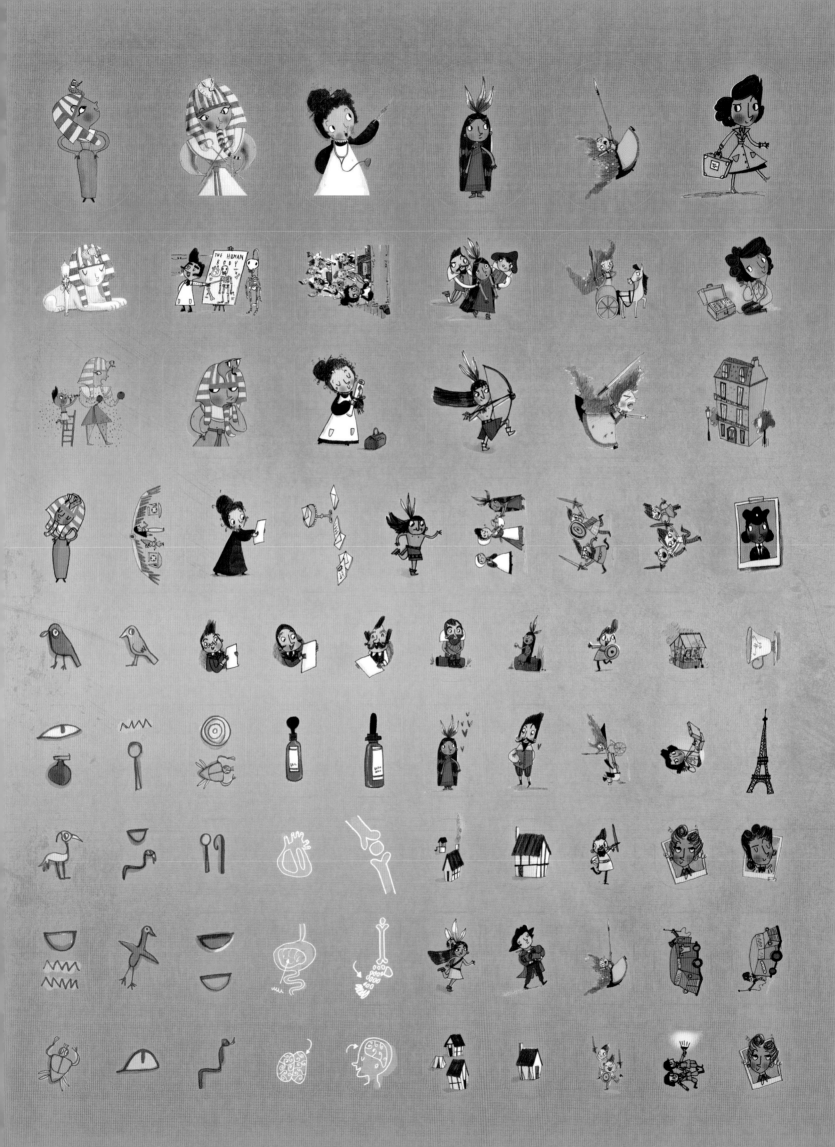

Ada Lovelace loved machines. She had such a fantastic imagination that, in the early **1800s**, she became the world's first computer programmer – over a century before the first computer was even built!

FLYOLOGY
BY ADA LOVELACE

Can you spot the difference between the two pictures? There are ten to find.

MAKE HISTORY WITH
HATSHEPSUT

Hatshepsut was the first female pharaoh to rule ancient Egypt. At the time, many people did not think women could be strong leaders but she proved them wrong and reigned for 20 years! To gain respect, Hatshepsut had statues of herself built. To show her people that women could be pharoahs, she portrayed herself looking like a masculine king with broad shoulders, a fake beard (which all traditional pharaohs wore) and a head cloth and a cobra.

If you were a mighty Egyptian pharaoh, how would you want to look? Draw yourself as an Egyptian statue!

Sayyida was the great queen of Tétouan and ruled the Mediterranean Sea with some of the most fearsome pirates of her time. She never let anyone tell her what to do and ruled as the undisputed pirate queen for over 30 years.

Make your own treasure map with Sayyida. Use stickers to decorate it.

Write for rights with Qiu Jin

"DO NOT tell me women are not the stuff of HEROES."

During Qiu Jin's life, Chinese women were forced to follow many old and outdated traditions. But Qiu Jin did not let this hold her back. She wrote powerful poems about the struggles women faced and campaigned for women's rights. She became a hero in China and inspired other women to make a change.

Write a poem about something you believe in. Decorate the page using stickers.

_____
_____
_____
_____
_____
_____
_____
_____

SHINE LIKE A STAR WITH
JOSEPHINE BAKER

Josephine Baker loved dancing and was part of one of the first Broadway shows with an all-black cast. In **1925**, she danced her way to France, where she heard that there was no segregation, so that everyone could enjoy her wonderful dance moves.

Colour in Josephine and Chiquita.

Segregation means keeping people separate — in the USA, segregation laws kept black and white people apart.

JOSEPHINE EVEN HAD HER OWN PET CHEETAH CALLED CHIQUITA!

Josephine loved lots of dazzling dance moves like the **Turkey Trot**, **The Itch**, the **Mess Around** and the **Charleston!** Draw and sticker Josephine dancing across the page.

"I improvised, CRAZED by the music... Each time I LEAPED I seemed to touch the sky!"

BRING YOUR IMAGINATION TO LIFE WITH

MARY WOLLSTONECRAFT & MARY SHELLEY

In **1792**, Mary Wollstonecraft published the first book suggesting that women's rights should be the same as men which caused quite a stir at the time.

Later, in **1818**, her daughter Mary Shelley shocked readers in a very different way. She wrote a chilling story called *Frankenstein*, which was all about the dangers of not thinking about your actions properly.

This mother and daughter duo were not afraid of being outspoken. Use the space to write your own story about a monster.

If you were an author, what would you write about?

A story always has a great hero. Who is the hero in your story?

You can include their name, what they look like and what makes them great.

The hero usually has to overcome a villain or an enemy. Who will they be in your story?

You can include their name, what they look like and what makes them so terrible.

A good story always has a great opening line. Can you finish the story?

"Do you believe in monsters?" said the strange, booming voice.

_____

_____

_____

_____

_____

_____

_____

_____

_____

_____

Draw a picture of your monster here!

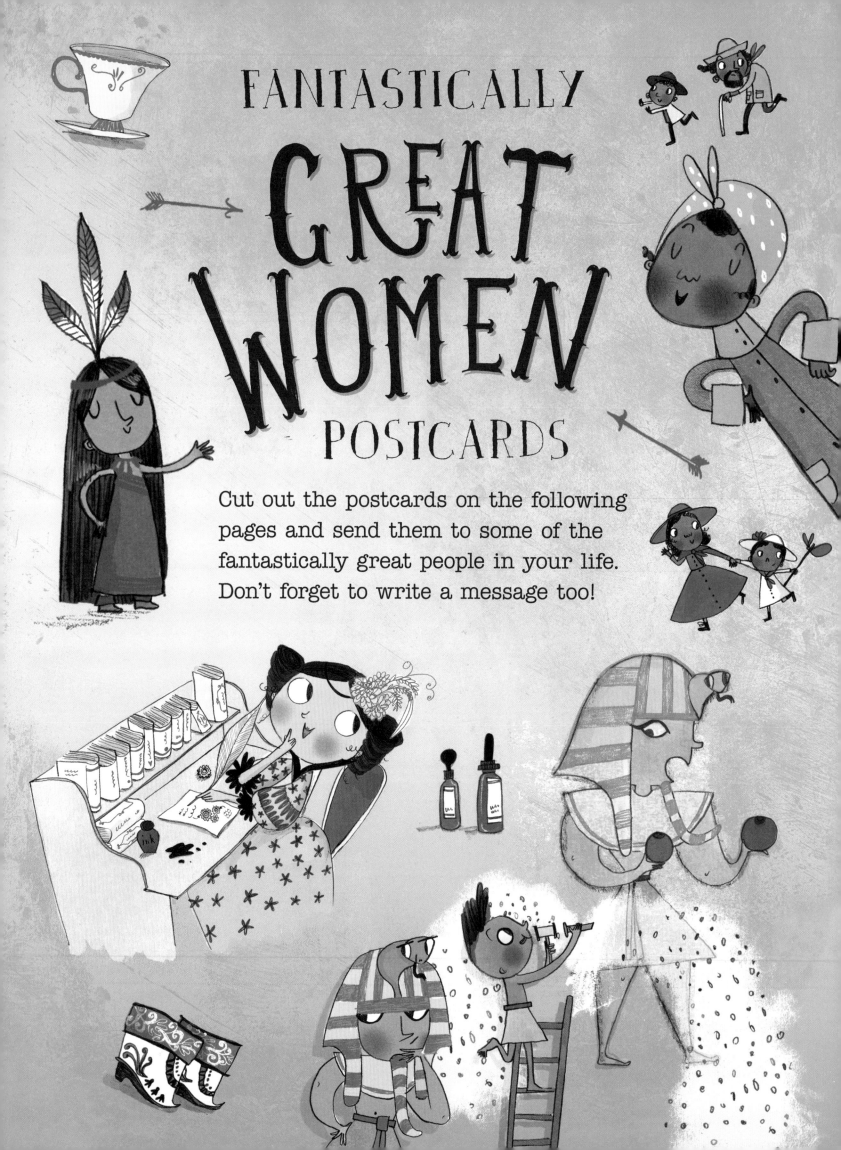

FANTASTICALLY GREAT WOMEN POSTCARDS

Cut out the postcards on the following pages and send them to some of the fantastically great people in your life. Don't forget to write a message too!

MARY SHELLEY

MARY WOLLSTONECRAFT

Sayyida al-Hurra

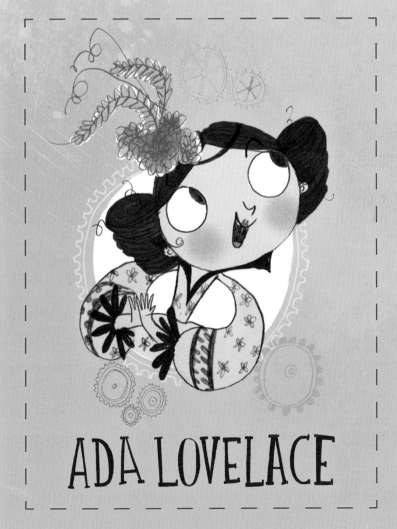

ADA LOVELACE

DR ELIZABETH BLACKWELL

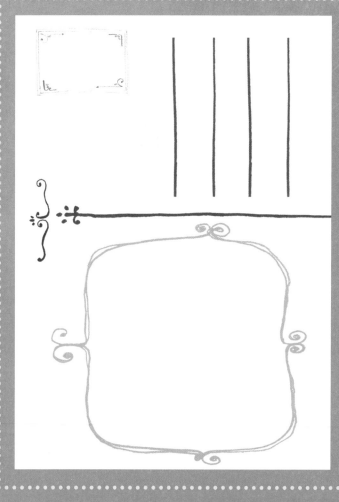
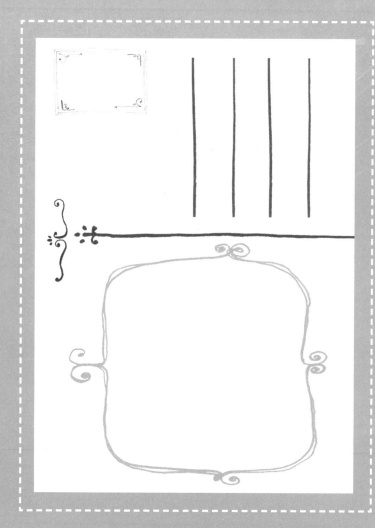
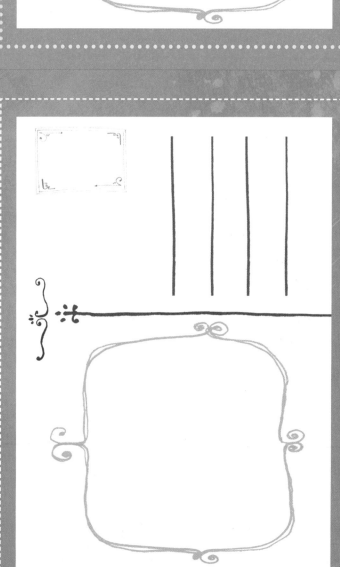
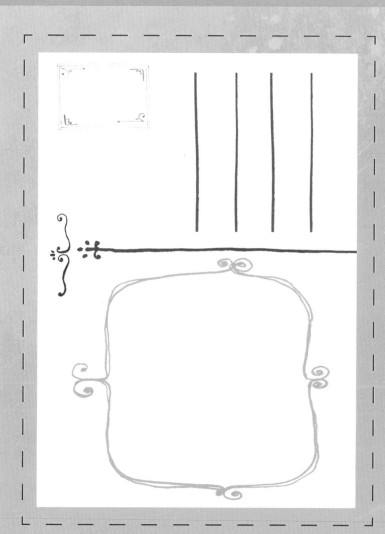

VALENTINA
TERESHKOVA

JOSEPHINE BAKER

HARRIET
TUBMAN

NOOR
INAYAT
KHAN

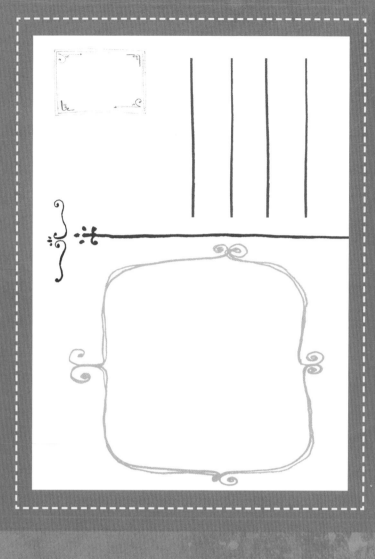
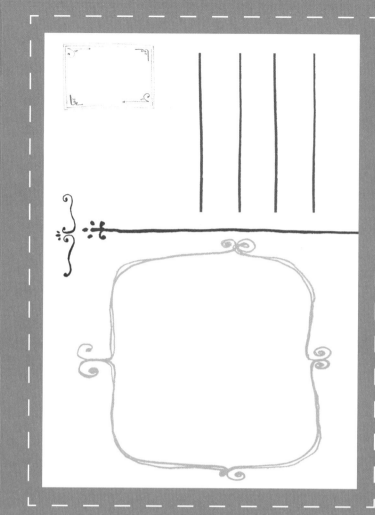
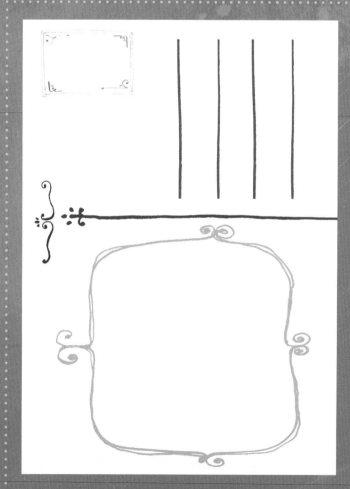
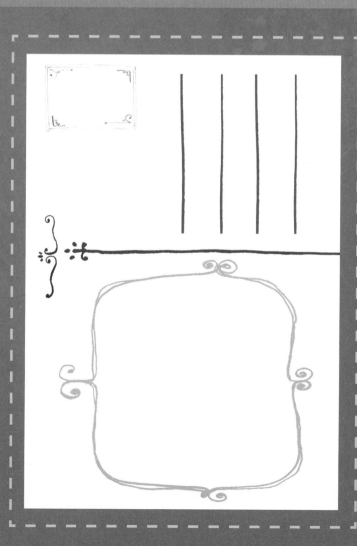

My Fantastically GREAT WOMEN

People can make history in lots of different ways. Draw someone you think changed history in this frame.

Name:

HOW ARE YOU GOING TO MAKE HISTORY?

BE THE LEADER OTHERS WANT TO FOLLOW!

The fantastically great women in this book believed anything was possible.

Write your own hopes and dreams for the future here.

_____

_____

_____

_____

_____

_____

_____

_____

SHINE like the STAR you are.

Be CURIOUS. Be BRAVE!

Be what you want to be!

Don't be afraid...

...of BIG ideas!

You are free to follow your own path.